Garfield Eats Crow

BY JIM DAVIS

Ballantine Books • New York

A Ballantine Book
Published by The Random House Publishing Group

Copyright © 2003 by PAWS, Incorporated. All Rights Reserved.

"GARFIELD" and the GARFIELD characters are registered and unregistered trademarks of PAWS, Inc.

All rights reserved under International and Pan-American Copyright Conventions. Published in the United States by Ballantine Books, an imprint of The Random House Publishing Group, a division of Random House, Inc., New York, and simultaneously in Canada by Random House of Canada Limited, Toronto.

Ballantine and colophon are registered trademarks of Random House, Inc.

www.ballantinebooks.com

Library of Congress Control Number: 2001119049

ISBN 0-345-45201-1

Manufactured in the United States of America

First Edition: January 2003

10 9 8 7 6 5 4

GARFIELD'S favorite games to play with Odie

Spin the Beagle

Volley Dog

Hide-and-Go-Away

Traffic Twister

Pin the Blame on the Puppy

Fetch the Ham

6

HI, I'M HOWIE THE HAPPY TURKEY!

BRRRR... I'M COLD! WOULD YOU PUT ME IN THE OVEN?

STOP IT, GARFIELD

I WANNA BE A SANDWICH!

ELLEN, THIS IS JON

CLICK

OH, NO! SOMEONE CUT HER PHONE LINE!

SOUNDS LIKE A JOB FOR DENIAL MAN

I REMEMBER THE MISCHIEF WE GOT INTO AS KIDS

WE'D SNEAK UP TO A HOUSE...

AND FLIP THEIR WELCOME MAT OVER!

AH, THAT WOULD EXPLAIN YOUR KEY COLLECTION

17

SLAM!

IT WAS HORRIBLE! I BARELY ESCAPED WITH MY LIFE!!

CHRISTMAS SHOPPING AT THE MALL

www.garfield.com

JIM DAVIS 12-18

GARFIELD!

JIM DAVIS 12-19

THAT WAS THE SHOPPING MALL CALLING!

SANTA'S ELF WANTS HIS BOOTIES BACK

THE CRYBABY

www.garfield.com

LOOK WHAT CAME, GARFIELD...A CHRISTMAS PACKAGE FROM MY MOM!

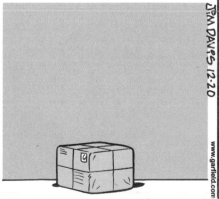

OKAY, I'M GOING TO CUT THE STRING...

CAREFUL... DON'T SPILL THE GRAVY

JIM DAVIS 12-20

www.garfield.com

HERE'S YOUR MAIL

AND HERE'S THE MAILMAN'S WALLET

LEAVE THE POOR MAN ALONE!

BOY, ARE HIS KIDS UGLY

JIM DAVIS 1-1

WHAT DO YOU WANT TO DO?

OKAY

JIM DAVIS 1-2

HOME IS WHERE YOU CAN WALK AROUND IN YOUR UNDERWEAR

JIM DAVIS 1-3

HOME IS WHERE YOU CAN DRINK MILK OUT OF THE CARTON

HOME IS WHERE YOU CAN SCRATCH WHERE IT ITCHES

HOME IS DISGUSTING

BEEN EATING THOSE FRUIT-SHAPED REFRIGERATOR MAGNETS AGAIN?

MAYBE

BAT
BAT

BAT
BAT
BAT

BAT
BAT
BAT

MY PARENTS WANTED ME TO BE A SWEATER, BUT NOOOOOO...

EMPIRES RISE AND FALL

SEE?!

WHY RISE?!

HELLO, IS EVELYN THERE?

WHAT'S THAT? SHE DOESN'T LIVE THERE ANYMORE?

SHE'S HOPPED A FREIGHTER FOR BORNEO?

SHE'S FORSWORN ALL HER MATERIAL POSSESSIONS AND MODERN WAYS OF LIVING?

WOW

SHE DIDN'T MENTION THAT ON OUR DATE LAST NIGHT

YOU DO HAVE THAT EFFECT ON WOMEN

JIM DAVIS 1-21

37

TODAY WASN'T A GOOD DAY

BUT I GUESS IT WASN'T A BAD DAY EITHER

SO YOU'RE SAYING IT WASN'T A DAY AT ALL

I'M NOT GOING TO SHED ANYMORE

I'VE CONTRACTED THE JOB OUT

OUT THERE ARE ALL OF NATURE'S WONDERS!

IN HERE ARE CORN CHIPS AND DIP

I WANT IT ALL!

FOMP

JIM DAVIS 1-28

HELLO, MOM

OH, THE SAME OLD THING

RIGHT NOW I'M DUSTING THE CAT

HEE HEE HEE

GARFIELD, I HEAR SOMETHING IN THE BASEMENT!

IT COULD BE A **HUGE** RAT!

DOESN'T THAT INFLAME YOUR PRIMAL INSTINCTS?

YES, I'LL BE IN THE CAR

RESERVED

RESERVED

IS IT POSSIBLE THAT I'VE LOST THE ELEMENT OF SURPRISE?

ODIE DUG UP THE FLOWERS IN THE GARDEN!

OOPS

ODIE DUG UP THE FLOWERS IN THE GARDEN!

JIM DAVIS 2-8

CONGRATULATIONS, YOU HAVE WON THE GRAND PRIZE!

AN EVENING WITH ME

THE EXCITEMENT WAS TOO MUCH

PROBABLY A STOMACH VIRUS

JIM DAVIS 2-9

NOBODY CAN STRETCH LIKE A CAT

JIM DAVIS 2-10

YAWN

HEY!

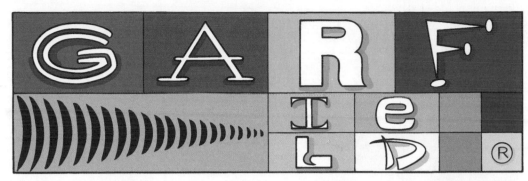

POOKY! YOU'RE WARM! YOU'VE BEEN HUGGED RECENTLY, AND **NOT** BY ME!

HAVE YOU BEEN HUGGING AROUND?!

I JUST GOT YOUR BEAR OUT OF THE DRYER

I'M SUCH A JEALOUS FOOL!

SLORP! SLURP! SLUP! SLURP!

PLEASE, GARFIELD, THERE'S NOTHING MORE DISGUSTING THAN THAT!

SLORP! SLUP!

EXCEPT THAT

GARFIELD, HELP! I LOCKED MYSELF OUT GETTING THE PAPER!

HURRY! I DON'T HAVE ANY PANTS ON!

I'M WEARING THE PUPPY UNDERWEAR!

THEN COME IN THROUGH THE PET DOOR

TOMORROW I'M GOING BACK TO GETTING DRESSED **AFTER** I TAKE MY SHOWER!

WELL, AT LEAST YOU TRIED SOMETHING

GARFIELD, WAS THAT THE BLENDER?

FORGET IT, I DON'T WANT TO KNOW

BUNNY-SLIPPER FRAPPÉ?

I KNOW HOW TO GET A WOMAN'S ATTENTION

WHO WANTS TO HEAR SOME BARNYARD IMITATIONS?!

WELL, THAT GOT HER ATTENTION

I DIDN'T KNOW ANYONE COULD RUN THAT FAST IN HEELS

HEH, HEH, HEH...

OH, THE TROUBLE I COULD CAUSE!

IF MY CLAWS WEREN'T STUCK IN THE TABLE

MY COFFEE'S COLD

BOY, I HATE COLD COFFEE. HATE IT. HATE IT. HATE IT

NOPE, THERE'S NOTHING IN THE WORLD WORSE THAN COLD COFFEE

SLAP SLAP SLAP

I'LL BET IF I TRIED AS HARD AS I COULD, I COULDN'T POSSIBLY THINK OF ANYTHING WORSE THAN COLD COFFEE

TWITCH TWITCH

EEEEYAAAAAAHHH!!!

SKREENK

OKAY... SOGGY SHORTS,— MAYBE

JIM DAVIS 5-11

ENJOY THE LITTLE THINGS, AND THE BIG THINGS WILL TAKE CARE OF THEMSELVES

JIM DAVIS 3-18

I'LL BE SHAVING, IN CASE ANYONE CALLS FOR ME

BUZZZZZZZZZZZZ

BUZZZZZZZZZZZZZZZZ

CLICK

JUST CHECKING... DID ANYONE CALL?

THE PARANOIA POLICE SEND THEIR REGARDS

JIM DAVIS 3-25

LIFE STINKS

YOU SHOULD HAVE A MORE POSITIVE ATTITUDE

LIFE STINKS

JIM DAVIS 3-26

I'M THINKING ABOUT WRITING THE STORY OF MY LIFE

MAYBE I SHOULD ACTUALLY DO SOMETHING FIRST

THAT WOULD REALLY HELP WITH THE TITLE

JIM DAVIS 3-27

REMEMBER THAT DAY AT THE AMUSEMENT PARK, GARFIELD?

HOW CAN I FORGET?

PHOTOS

JIM DAVIS 3-28

THEY SURE HAD SOME SCARY RIDES

EMBARRASSING...

PHOTOS

I COULDN'T STOP SCREAMING

BUT, IN THE PARKING LOT, JON?

PHOTOS

WHEN COMMUNICATING WITH PETS...

KEEP COMMANDS SIMPLE AND TO THE POINT

LOSE... SOME... WEIGHT

GET... A... LIFE

MAYBE I'LL GET TOGETHER WITH FRIENDS TONIGHT

WE'LL LAUGH AND ENGAGE IN STIMULATING CONVERSATION...

OR MAYBE I'LL STAY HOME AND FLOSS

REALITY SETS IN

DO YOU KNOW WHAT'S WRONG WITH CATS?

THEY...

CLICK

HEY!

YOU WATCH TOO MUCH TELEVISION

WE SHOULD DO SOMETHING

HOW ABOUT MAILING MRS. FEENY'S LITTLE DOG TO AN OBSCURE OVERSEAS NATION WITH INSUFFICIENT POSTAGE?

OR WE COULD THUMB WRESTLE FOR THAT LAST PIECE OF CHEESECAKE

OR WE COULD HIJACK AN ICE CREAM TRUCK AND HOLD THE DRIVER HOSTAGE FOR THE WORLD'S LARGEST NUTTY-BUDDY

OR WE COULD PAINT OURSELVES PURPLE, SIT IN THE BATHTUB TOO LONG, AND PRETEND WE'RE RAISINS

CHECKERS?

I'M RED THIS TIME

JIM DAVIS 4-1

WOOF

UH... GARFIELD?...

YES, I KNOW. THEY'RE MAKING DOGS SMALLER THESE DAYS, AREN'T THEY?

JIM DAVIS 4·5

SNAP!

OUCH!

JIM DAVIS 4·6

SNAP!

OUCH!

SNAP!

OUCH!

HE'LL GIVE UP, EVENTUALLY

MAY I HAVE THE BAIT?

WE NEED A FOURTH FOR BRIDGE

JIM DAVIS 4·7

OKAY, BUT THIS TIME WE USE MY CARDS

LAST GAME I ABOUT WENT BLIND

YOU'RE GOING TO HURT ME NOW, AREN'T YOU?

UNLESS YOU ACT POSTHASTE TO RECTIFY THIS UNFORTUNATE SITUATION

JIM DAVIS 4·8

I GOT YOU A SURPRISE, GARFIELD!

BUT I CAN'T FIND IT

IT WOULDN'T HAVE MAYBE, SORTA, KINDA RESEMBLED A (BURP) BOX OF DONUTS, WOULD IT?

MY DATE SAID SHE HATES ME MORE THAN ALMOST ANYTHING

ALMOST ANYTHING

I CAUGHT THAT

I AM BORED, GARFIELD

I NEED SOME EXCITEMENT

MAYBE I'LL SIT ON THE ROOF!

JOOOON?! THE FIRE DEPARTMENT SAID NEVER DO THAT AGAIN

GOOD TO SEE YOU AGAIN, SON. YOU'RE LOOKING WELL

THANKS... YOU TOO, DAD

WELL, GOT CHORES TO DO

BETTER GO UNPACK

(SNIFF) A REAL FATHER-SON MOMENT

GARFIELD ISN'T MUCH FOR THE FARM LIFE, IS HE, JONNY?

I GUESS NOT, MOM

BUT HE'LL LEARN TO COPE

AAAGGHH!

ONLY THREE CHANNELS?!!

SEE THAT, GARFIELD? THOSE ARE SHEEP

LOOK LIKE DUST BUNNIES WITH LEGS

THAT'S WHERE WOOL COMES FROM

HOLD ON...

IF THIS IS ANYTHING LIKE THAT CHICKEN/EGG THING, I DON'T WANNA KNOW

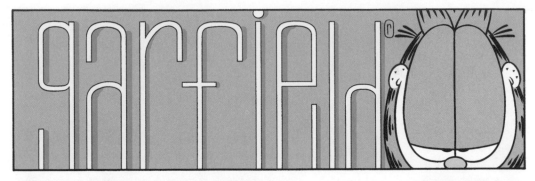

THIS ROOM WOULD LOOK BETTER WITH LESS CAT HAIR

THERE'S NO CAT HAIR IN HERE EXCEPT WHAT'S ON ME

HEY!

THIS IS MRS. SPITTLE, MY THIRD-GRADE TEACHER

SHE HATED ME. SHE MADE ME TAKE SUMMER SCHOOL

SHE WAS OKAY, I GUESS

...THUS THE LOVINGLY RENDERED HORNS, GOATEE, AND BLACKED-OUT TOOTH...

PLAY DEAD, ODIE!

GOOD BOY!

NOW, STAY

A GREAT NEW STORE OPENED UP, GARFIELD!

IT'S CALLED "CREATE-A-PET"

I NOW HAVE A BUNNY!

WHO MAIMS

HEY, TINA, I'M THROWING A PARTY SATURDAY NIGHT. WANT TO COME?

YEEES, I'LL BE THERE

PARTY POOPER

GARFIELD, WEEKENDS ARE MY TIME TO REAR BACK AND HOWL!

CLOSE

...LIE DOWN AND GIGGLE?

CLOSER

...CRAWL INTO A FETAL POSITION AND WHIMPER?

THERE YOU GO

IF SLEEPING IS AN ART, THEN I'M A MASTERPIECE

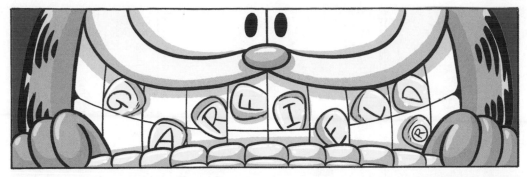

HERE ARE YOUR MENUS, HON

I LOVE DINERS

OOOH, I HAVE HEARTBURN ALREADY!

I'M IN DEEP-FRIED HEAVEN

HMM...THE THREE-BEAN BURRITO LOOKS GOOD...

SORRY, WE'RE OUT OF THAT

I OWE YOU ONE, IRMA

WOULD YOU LIKE EXTRA HORSERADISH SAUCE ON YOUR GARLIC-ONION-SARDINE SANDWICH?

SURE

NO GOODNIGHT KISS FOR YOU

YOU KNOW YOU'RE A NERD WHEN...

You think playing the accordion makes you look "hot"

In school, you were voted "Most Likely to Marry a Kitchen Appliance"

You own an extensive collection of bunny slippers

The last CD you bought was "Best of the Harmonicats"

You take your mom to the prom

You alphabetize your sock drawer

STRIPS, SPECIALS, OR BESTSELLING BOOKS...

GARFIELD'S ON EVERYONE'S MENU

Don't miss even one episode in the Tubby Tabby's hilarious series!

GARFIELD AT LARGE **New larger, full-color format!**
....(#1) 0-345-44382-9
GARFIELD GAINS WEIGHT **New larger, full-color format!**
....(#2) 0-345-44975-4
GARFIELD BIGGER THAN LIFE **New larger, full-color format!**
....(#3) 0-345-45027-2
GARFIELD WEIGHS IN **New larger, full-color format!**
....(#4) 0-345-45205-4
GARFIELD TAKES THE CAKE ....(#5) 0-345-44978-9
GARFIELD EATS HIS HEART OUT ....(#6) 0-345-32018-2
GARFIELD SITS AROUND THE HOUSE ...(#7) 0-345-32011-5
GARFIELD TIPS THE SCALES ....(#8) 0-345-33580-5
GARFIELD LOSES HIS FEET ....(#9) 0-345-31805-6
GARFIELD MAKES IT BIG ....(#10) 0-345-31928-1
GARFIELD ROLLS ON ....(#11) 0-345-32634-2
GARFIELD OUT TO LUNCH.....................(#12) 0-345-33118-4
GARFIELD FOOD FOR THOUGHT..........(#13) 0-345-34129-5
GARFIELD SWALLOWS HIS PRIDE........(#14) 0-345-34725-0
GARFIELD WORLDWIDE.........................(#15) 0-345-35158-4
GARFIELD ROUNDS OUT ....(#16) 0-345-35388-9
GARFIELD CHEWS THE FAT ....(#17) 0-345-35956-9
GARFIELD GOES TO WAIST....................(#18) 0-345-36430-9
GARFIELD HANGS OUT ....(#19) 0-345-36835-5
GARFIELD TAKES UP SPACE ....(#20) 0-345-37029-5
GARFIELD SAYS A MOUTHFUL................(#21) 0-345-37368-5
GARFIELD BY THE POUND ....(#22) 0-345-37579-3
GARFIELD KEEPS HIS CHINS UP ....(#23) 0-345-37959-4
GARFIELD TAKES HIS LICKS ....(#24) 0-345-38170-X
GARFIELD HITS THE BIG TIME..............(#25) 0-345-38332-X

GARFIELD PULLS HIS WEIGHT ....(#26) 0-345-38666-3
GARFIELD DISHES IT OUT ....(#27) 0-345-39287-6
GARFIELD LIFE IN THE FAT LANE ....(#28) 0-345-39776-2
GARFIELD TONS OF FUN.......................(#29) 0-345-40386-X
GARFIELD BIGGER AND BETTER..........(#30) 0-345-40770-9
GARFIELD HAMS IT UP..........................(#31) 0-345-41241-9
GARFIELD THINKS BIG ....(#32) 0-345-41671-6
GARFIELD THROWS HIS WEIGHT AROUND
....(#33) 0-345-42749-1
GARFIELD LIFE TO THE FULLEST.........(#34) 0-345-43239-8
GARFIELD FEEDS THE KITTY ....(#35) 0-345-43673-3
GARFIELD HOGS THE SPOTLIGHT ....(#36) 0-345-43922-8
GARFIELD BEEFS UP.............................(#37) 0-345-44109-5
GARFIELD GETS COOKIN'......................(#38) 0-345-44582-1
GARFIELD EATS CROW..........................(#39) 0-345-45201-1

GARFIELD AT HIS SUNDAY BEST!

GARFIELD TREASURY 0-345-32106-5
THE SECOND GARFIELD TREASURY..............0-345-33276-8
THE THIRD GARFIELD TREASURY 0-345-32635-0
THE FOURTH GARFIELD TREASURY 0-345-34726-9
THE FIFTH GARFIELD TREASURY 0-345-36268-3
THE SIXTH GARFIELD TREASURY 0-345-37367-7
THE SEVENTH GARFIELD TREASURY...........0-345-38427-X
THE EIGHTH GARFIELD TREASURY 0-345-39778-9
THE NINTH GARFIELD TREASURY 0-345-41670-8
THE TENTH GARFIELD TREASURY 0-345-43674-1

AND DON'T MISS...

GARFIELD AT 25: IN DOG YEARS I'D BE DEAD
....0-345-45530-4